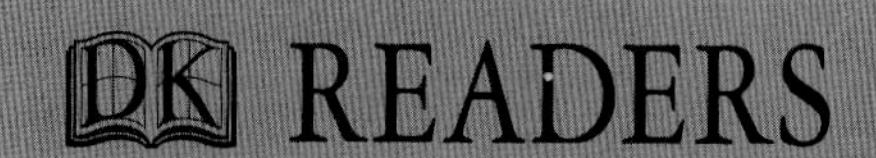

Surprise Puppy!

Written by Judith Walker-Hodge

DK
A Dorling Kindersley Book

On Friday afternoon,
Dad brought home
a surprise.

"Look what I've got," he said.
"It's a puppy!
He belongs
to a friend
of mine."

"Will you help look after him for a week?"

"Yes! Yes!" shouted the twins.

puppy

"The puppy's wagging his tail," said Sam.

"That means he likes us," said Jessica.

"My friend wants you to give him a name," Dad told the twins.

"I want to call him Wags," said Jessica

"Wags is a good name," said Sam. "He wags his tail a lot."

Wags ran around the room.

“He wants to play,” said Dad.
“He needs lots of exercise.”

Sam looked in the box of things that had come with Wags.
He found a toy ball.

He threw the ball
into the garden.
"Fetch," he called.

Wags chased the ball, but ...

... he did not bring it back.

He just sat
by the ball and
wagged his tail!

"Wags doesn't know
how to fetch," said Jessica.

"Let's teach him this weekend," said Sam.

"Good idea," said Dad. "Then next week you can show my friend what he can do."

Later that evening,
Dad couldn't find
his slippers.

"Oh no!" cried Jessica.
"Wags has got your slippers.
He's chewing them!"

"He's teething,"
Dad told her.

"Give him a dog chew.
There's one in the box
with his things."

Soon it was bedtime.
"Can Wags sleep with me?"
Sam asked.

"Wags is too young," said Dad.
"He has to sleep in the kitchen."

"Put some newspaper
on the floor in case
he makes a mess."

“Make sure
he has water,”
said Dad.

“Then lay a blanket
in his basket
to keep him warm.”

On Saturday morning,
the twins rushed
into the kitchen.

Wags jumped up at them.
He was pleased
to see them.

“Get down, Wags,”
said Mum.
“Puppies must learn
not to jump up
at people.”

"Do puppies eat cornflakes?"
asked Sam.

"Don't be silly.
Puppies eat puppy food,"
said Jessica.
"Mum is feeding Wags now."

Mum filled Wags's
food bowl
with puppy food.

Then she filled
his water bowl
with fresh water.

That afternoon,
they went to the vet.
Wags needed a check-up.

"Why do you need
to check Wags?" asked Sam.

“To make sure
he is healthy,”
said the vet.

The vet checked Wags carefully.

“Wags has a shiny coat
and a wet nose.
That means
he’s well,”
she said.

On Sunday,
the family took Wags
for a long walk.
They went to the park.

Sam and Jessica took turns holding the lead.

"I wish we had a puppy," said Jessica.

"Puppies are hard work," Dad told her.

"We don't mind!" shouted the twins.

lead

After the walk,
everyone went indoors.

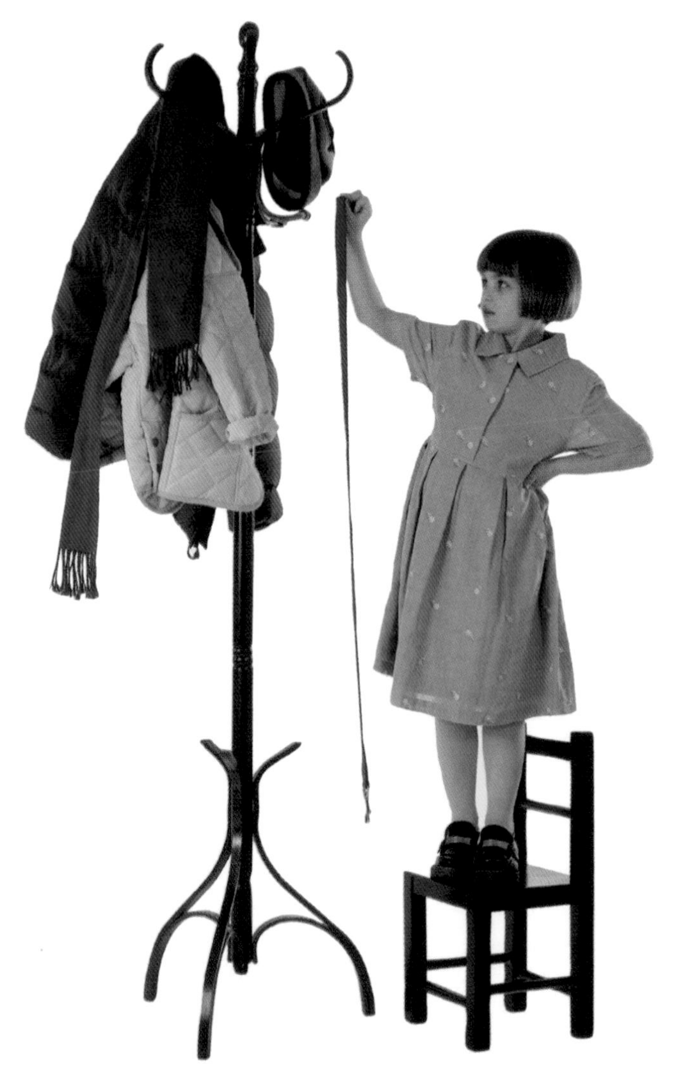

Jessica hung Wags's lead
on the coat rack.

Sam put some fresh water in the water bowl.

No one noticed that the gate was open.

No one ...
except Wags!

"Where's Wags?"
Dad asked
a few minutes later.

"Oh no,
the gate's open!"
cried Jessica.
"Wags has
run away."

"Come on,
let's find him,"
said Mum.

But he wasn't on the street.

And he wasn't in the park.

"I've found him!" called Jessica.
Wags was next door.
He had been rolling
in the mud.

They brought him home and
gave him a bath.

"We have to keep
the gate shut,"
Mum told
the twins.

"Okay," said Jessica
as she dried Wags with a towel.

"Sorry," said Sam.
Then he brushed Wags
with a dog brush.

On Monday, it was the twins' birthday.

Mum gave them a tiny box and Jessica opened it.

"It's a tag!" she said. "It has our address on it ... and it says WAGS!"

"It's a dog tag,"
said Dad.
"Wags belongs
to you two now.
This weekend was a test.
You passed with flying colours!"

Glossary

Chew
a hard piece of material that a dog chews

Dog tag
a metal disc with the dog's name and address

Lead
a long line clipped to a dog's collar

Puppy
a young dog in its first year

Vet
a person who examines animals